Contents

Step 1: Two-digit addition no carrying

When learning written addition, it is important to know how to set numbers out vertically with the correct digits in the correct columns. Here, 56 and 33 are correctly written under the Tens and Units headings.

What to do

$56 + 33 = ?$

T	U
5	6
+ 3	3

1 Set out the numbers in the correct columns with one digit in each square.

2 Always start at the right-hand side, with the units column! Add the top and bottom digits. $6 + 3 = 9$

	T	U
	5	6
+	3	3
		9

3 Next move to the left and look at the digits in the tens column. Add the top and bottom digits. 5 tens + 3 tens = 8 tens

	T	U
	5	6
+	3	3
	8	9

4 Finally, look at the answer and check whether it seems a sensible answer. You can subtract one of the numbers in the question from the answer to see if it gives you the other number. $89 - 33 = 56$. Yes, this is correct.

	T	U
	8	9
−	3	3
	5	6

Now you try

1 $25 + 44 = ?$

	T	U
	2	5
+	4	4
		9

2 $47 + 31 = ?$

	T	U
	4	7
+	3	1
		8

3 $61 + 25 = ?$

	T	U
	6	1
+	2	5

4 $54 + 23 = ?$

	T	U
	5	4
+	2	3

5 $77 + 22 = ?$

	T	U
	7	7
+	2	2

6 $53 + 45 = ?$

	T	U
	5	3
+	4	5

More practice

Set out these questions yourself to answer them.

7 35 + 54 = ?

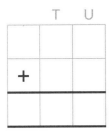

8 65 + 23 = ?

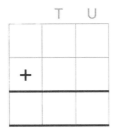

9 38 + 41 = ?

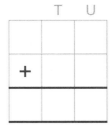

Problem solving

10 Ahmed bought a T-shirt costing £23 and a pair of jeans costing £42. What was the total cost?

_____

11 Find the total of 24 and 72.

_____

12 Dina is 23 years old. Her gran is 46 years older than she is. How old is her gran?

_____

13 The height of Li's cat is 23cm. Li's dog is 61cm taller than her cat. What is the height of Li's dog?

_____

14 Sam collects stickers. He has 45 stickers in one book and 52 in another. How many stickers is that altogether?

_____

15 What is the sum of 36 and 62?

_____

How did I find Step 1? ☐ Easy ☐ OK ☐ Difficult

Step 2: Three-digit addition no carrying

For three-digit numbers, work in the same way. Make sure the numbers are set out in the correct columns in the same way. Here, 526 and 143 are correctly written under the Hundreds, Tens and Units headings.

What to do

526 + 143 = ?

1 Set out the numbers in the correct columns with one digit in each square.

	H	T	U
	5	2	6
+	1	4	3

2 Always start at the right-hand side, with the units column! Add both units digits. 6 + 3 = 9

	5	2	6
+	1	4	3
			9

3 Next move to the left and look at the digits in the tens column. Add both tens digits. 2 + 4 = 6

	5	2	6
+	1	4	3
		6	9

4 Then move to the left again and add both hundreds digits. 5 + 1 = 6

5 Finally, look at the answer and check whether it seems a sensible answer. 669 – 143 = 526, which is correct!

	5	2	6
+	1	4	3
	6	6	9

Now you try

1 483 + 414 = ?

	H	T	U
	4	8	3
+	4	1	4
			7

2 575 + 214 = ?

	H	T	U
	5	7	5
+	2	1	4
			9

3 652 + 325 = ?

	H	T	U
	6	5	2
+	3	2	5
			7

4 753 + 241 = ?

	H	T	U
	7	5	3
+	2	4	1

5 535 + 224 = ?

	H	T	U
	5	3	5
+	2	2	4

6 304 + 264 = ?

	H	T	U
	3	0	4
+	2	6	4

More practice

Set out these questions yourself to answer them.

7 465 + 123 = ?

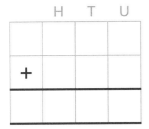

8 842 + 145 = ?

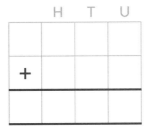

9 735 + 123 = ?

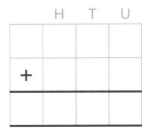

10 631 + 264 = ?

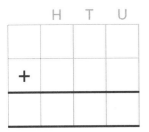

11 455 + 323 = ?

12 573 + 402 = ?

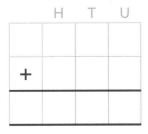

Problem solving

13 A farmer had 624 sheep. He bought 315 more of them at market. How many sheep has he now?

14 Kim had £468 in a bank account. She paid in an extra £221. How much money is in the bank account now?

15 Two numbers have a difference of 233. If the smaller number is 542, what is the larger number?

16 604 adults and 173 children went to a football match. How many people is this in total?

How did I find Step 2? ☐ Easy ☐ OK ☐ Difficult

Step 3: Three-digit addition carrying I ten

The digits in the units column of these questions
have a total that is greater than 9.

See here that 7 add 5 is greater than 9!

H	T	U
	5	3	7
+	I	4	5

What to do

$537 + 145 = ?$

1   Start with adding the units. 7 + 5 = 12. Write the 2 in
    the units column and carry the ten units over to become
    I ten. Write I below the answer line, in the tens column.

H	T	U
	5	3	7
+	I	4	5
			2

2   Now add the digits in the tens column and remember
    to add the I ten you carried. 3 tens + 4 tens plus the
    I ten you carried is 8 tens. Write 8 in the tens column.

	5	3	7
+	I	4	5
		8	2

3   Then add the hundreds digits. 5 + I = 6. Write 6 in
    the hundreds column to complete the answer.

	5	3	7
+	I	4	5
	6	8	2

Now you try

1

	5	3	4
+	I	5	8
			2

2

	7	2	6
+	2	3	4
			0

3

	5	5	5
+	4	I	5
			0

4

	7	I	4
+	2	5	7

5

	6	3	3
+	2	3	9

6

	4	2	9
+	I	6	5

More practice

7
```
    8  3  6
+   1  5  7
_____
```

8
```
    5  4  8
+   2  4  8
_____
```

9
```
    4  0  9
+   3  6  7
_____
```

10
```
    7  3  5
+   1  4  7
_____
```

11
```
    5  3  8
+   2  3  6
_____
```

12
```
    3  2  4
+   2  1  8
_____
```

Set out these questions yourself to answer them.

13 435 + 128 = ?

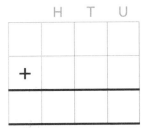

14 506 + 447 = ?

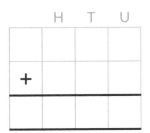

15 574 + 406 = ?

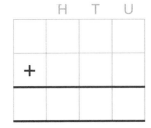

Problem solving

16 Online, a TV costs £548. In a high street shop the same TV costs £128 more. How much does it cost in the shop?

17 Two numbers have a difference of 733. If the smaller number is 127, what is the larger number?

How did I find Step 3?   ☐ Easy   ☐ OK   ☐ Difficult

Step 4: Three-digit addition carrying 1 hundred

As for Step 3, these questions have two digits that have a total greater than 9, but this time the digits are in the tens column.

See here that 8 plus 8 is greater than 9!

H	T	U
	5	8	3
+	2	8	5

What to do

583 + 285 = ?

1 Start at the right-hand side, with the units! Add both units digits. 3 + 5 = 8

H	T	U
	5	8	3
+	2	8	5
			8

2 Then move left to the tens. 8 + 8 = 16. Write the 6 in the tens column and carry the 10 tens over to become 1 hundred. Write 1 below the line, in the hundreds column.

H	T	U
	5	8	3
+	2	8	5
		6	8
1			

3 Now add the digits in the hundreds column and remember to add the 1 you carried. 5 hundreds + 2 hundreds plus the 1 hundred you carried is 8 hundreds. Write 8 in the hundreds column to complete the answer.

H	T	U
	5	8	3
+	2	8	5
	8	6	8
1			

Now you try

1

	5	8	3
+	1	4	2
		2	5
	1		

2

	6	7	3
+	2	7	6
		4	9
	1		

3

	7	8	2
+	1	8	5
			7
	1		

4

	4	5	4
+	2	8	2
			6
	1		

5

	3	9	1
+	3	8	6

6

	4	6	2
+	1	7	7

More practice

7
```
    6  8  5
+   2  4  4
_____
```

8
```
    3  7  2
+   2  3  4
_____
```

9
```
    4  6  1
+   4  5  7
_____
```

Set out these questions yourself to answer them.

10 473 + 174 = ?

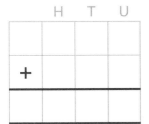

11 382 + 264 = ?

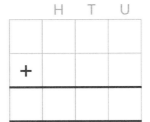

12 742 + 192 = ?

Problem solving

13 What is 452 more than 396?

14 A touch-screen computer costs £352 in a sale. The sale price is £184 less than it was before the sale. How much did it cost before the sale?

15 Ahmed climbed a mountain. He stopped for a rest 475m above sea level. The summit of the mountain was 392m higher than he was at that point. How high above sea level was the summit?

How did I find Step 4? ☐ Easy   ☐ OK   ☐ Difficult

Step 5: Three-digit addition carrying once, including answers greater than 999

On these pages, you must decide whether to carry a ten and/or a hundred. Look for when the digits in a column have a total greater than 9. Also, answers on these pages may be greater than 999.

What to do

673 + 655 = ?

1 Start at the right-hand side, with the units! Add both units digits.
3 + 5 = 8

Th	H	T	U
	6	7	3
+	6	5	5
			8

2 Then move left to the tens. 7 + 5 = 12. Write the 2 in the tens column and carry the 10 tens over to become 1 hundred. Write 1 below the line, in the hundreds column.

	6	7	3
+	6	5	5
		2	8
	1		

3 Now add the digits in the hundreds column and remember to add the 1 you carried. 6 hundreds + 6 hundreds plus the 1 hundred you carried is 13 hundreds. If there are no more digits to add, just write 1 in the thousands column and 3 in the hundreds column to complete the answer.

	6	7	3
+	6	5	5
1	3	2	8
	1		

Now you try

1

	2	3	6
+	9	4	5
		8	1
		1	

2

	9	7	4
+	4	6	4
		3	8
		1	

3

	4	9	3
+	1	9	5
			8
		1	

4

	6	5	7
+	6	2	4
			1
	1		

5

	7	2	8
+	3	0	6

6

	8	8	2
+	1	7	4

More practice

Set out these questions yourself to answer them.

7 678 + 714 = ?

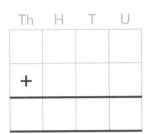

Th	H	T	U
+			

8 384 + 225 = ?

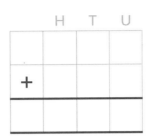

H	T	U
+		

9 918 + 712 = ?

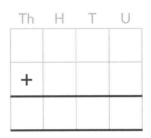

Th	H	T	U
+			

Problem solving

10 Work out the missing digit in this addition.

	4	◯	9
+	9	2	5
1	3	8	4

11 What is the sum of 825 and 567?

12 A school has 375 girls and 432 boys. How many pupils does it have in total?

13 How many is 426 plus 849?

14 Class M did a traffic survey. They saw 563 cars and 518 other vehicles in one day. How many vehicles did they see altogether that day?

| **How did I find Step 5?** | ☐ Easy | ☐ OK | ☐ Difficult |

Step 6: Three-digit addition of three numbers carrying once

On these pages, the questions involve adding three numbers. This means that sometimes you must carry more than 1 ten or more than 1 hundred.

What to do

$629 + 619 + 233 = ?$

	Th	H	T	U
		6	2	9
		6	1	9
+		2	3	3
				1
			2	

1 Start at the right-hand side, with the units! Add all the units digits. $9 + 9 + 3 = 21$. Write the 1 in the units column and carry the 20 over to become 2 tens. Write 2 below the line, in the tens column.

	H	T	U
	6	2	9
	6	1	9
+	2	3	3
		8	1
		2	

2 Now add the digits in the tens column and remember to add the 2 you carried. 2 tens + 1 ten + 3 tens plus the 2 tens carried = 8 tens. Write the 8 in the tens column.

	Th	H	T	U
		6	2	9
		6	1	9
+		2	3	3
	1	4	8	1
			2	

3 Now add the hundreds digits. 6 hundreds + 6 hundreds + 2 hundreds = 14 hundreds. If there are no more digits to add, just write 1 in the thousands column and 4 in the hundreds column to complete the answer.

Now you try

1

		7	4	8
		5	0	8
	+	1	2	8
				4
			2	

2

		5	3	7
		5	3	3
	+	4	2	2
				2
			1	

3

		8	7	2
		2	7	0
	+	1	7	3
				5
			2	

4

		3	9	4
		3	5	1
	+	1	9	3
				8
			2	

5

		7	1	8
		3	4	8
	+	2	1	4
			2	

6

		9	7	6
		7	4	1
	+	5	4	2

More practice

Set out these questions yourself to answer them.

7 514 + 207 + 228 = ?

Th	H	T	U
+			

8 781 + 282 + 196 = ?

Th	H	T	U
+			

Problem solving

9 Can you work out what digits the letters A and B stand for in this addition?

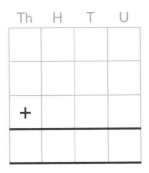

	A	B	A
	B	B	A
+	B	B	A
D	A	C	B

D

10 164 men, 173 women and 271 children were at a concert. How many people is that altogether?

11 Mrs Brown put 245g of flour, 108g of sugar and 225g of butter into a bowl and mixed it. How heavy is the mixture in total?

How did I find Step 6?   ☐ Easy   ☐ OK   ☐ Difficult

Check-up test 1 Two- and three-digit addition, including carrying once

Step 1

1 72 + 26 = ?

	7	2
+	2	6

2 55 + 23 = ?

	5	5
+	2	3

3 63 + 24 = ?

+		

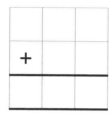

Step 2

4 543 + 251 = ?

	5	4	3
+	2	5	1

5 732 + 234 = ?

	7	3	2
+	2	3	4

6 134 + 464 = ?

+			

Step 3

7 428 + 358 = ?

	4	2	8
+	3	5	8

8 429 + 165 = ?

	4	2	9
+	1	6	5

9 635 + 128 = ?

+			

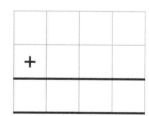

Steps 4 and 5

10 391 + 386 = ?

	3	9	1
+	3	8	6

11 462 + 977 = ?

	4	6	2
+	9	7	7

12 775 + 474 = ?

+			

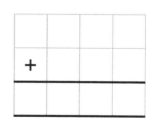

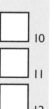

Step 6

13 718 + 348 + 214 = ?

	7	1	8
	3	4	8
+	2	1	4

14 855 + 741 + 542 = ?

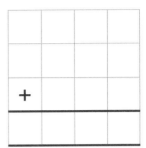

☐ 13

☐ 14

Steps 1 to 6 mixed

Use the grid below for working.

15 The height of Sue's cat is 25cm. Sue's dog is 61cm taller than her cat. What is the height of her dog?   _____   ☐ 15

16 An iPad costs £352 online. In a shop it costs £184 more than this. What does it cost in the shop?   _____   ☐ 16

17 How many more than one thousand is the total of 281, 456 and 302?   _____   ☐ 17

Total test score

Score	1	2	3	4	5	6	7	8	9	10	11	12	13	14	15	16	17
%	6	12	18	24	29	35	41	47	53	59	65	71	76	82	88	94	100

17

Step 7: Four-digit addition carrying once

	Th	H	T	U
	4	7	2	4
+	1	5	3	5

Here you will add four-digit numbers. You will need to carry once in each calculation. Look out for when the digits in a column have a total greater than 9. ⟶

What to do

4724 + 1535 = ?

1   Add the units digits. 4 + 5 = 9

	Th	H	T	U
	4	7	2	4
+	1	5	3	5
				9

2   Then move left to add the tens digits.
2 tens + 3 tens = 5 tens

	Th	H	T	U
	4	7	2	4
+	1	5	3	5
			5	9

3   Now add the digits in the hundreds column.
7 hundreds + 5 hundreds is 12 hundreds. Write the
2 in the hundreds column and carry the 10 hundreds
over to become 1 thousand. Write 1 below the line,
in the thousands column.

	Th	H	T	U
	4	7	2	4
+	1	5	3	5
		2	5	9
1				

4   Now add the thousands and remember to add the
1 you carried. 4 thousands + 1 thousand plus the
1 thousand you carried is 6 thousands. Write 6 in
the thousands column to complete the answer.

	Th	H	T	U
	4	7	2	4
+	1	5	3	5
	6	2	5	9
1				

Now you try

1

	4	4	5	8
+	1	4	8	0
			3	8
		1		

2

	5	6	2	9
+	1	2	1	6
				5
			1	

3

	3	4	7	0
+	3	3	6	3
				3

4

	4	8	5	3
+	1	7	3	2
				5

More practice

5
```
    5 9 2 4
  + 1 7 3 2
  _____

  _____
```

6
```
    6 2 9 3
  + 3 6 9 1
  _____

  _____
```

Set out these questions yourself to answer them.

7 2461 + 2263 = ?

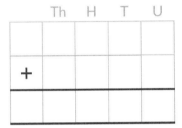

8 3925 + 3574 = ?

Th	H	T	U
+			

Problem solving

9 A pilot travelled 4323km on Monday. He rested on Tuesday and then flew 4762km on Wednesday. How many kilometres was this in total?

10 At a rugby match there were 3444 home fans and 1472 away fans. How many fans were there altogether?

11 Each letter in this sum stands for a different digit. Using spare paper for working, can you work out what each letter could stand for? **BAKE + CAKE = 9828**

| How did I find Step 7? | ☐ Easy | ☐ OK | ☐ Difficult |

Step 8: Three-digit addition carrying twice

On these pages, you will learn how to carry a ten and a hundred. Look for when the digits in a column have a total greater than 9.

What to do

687 + 585 = ?

1 Start at the right. Add both units digits. 7 + 5 = 12. Write the 2 in the units column and carry the ten units over to become 1 ten. Write 1 below the line, in the tens column.

Th	H	T	U
	6	8	7
+	5	8	5
			2
		1	

2 Then move left to add the tens digits and remember to add the 1 you carried. 8 tens + 8 tens plus the 1 ten carried is 17 tens. Write the 7 in the tens column and carry the 10 tens over to become 1 hundred. Write 1 below the line, in the hundreds column.

	6	8	7
+	5	8	5
		7	2
	1	1	

3 Now add the digits in the hundreds column and remember to add the 1 you carried. 6 hundreds + 5 hundreds plus the 1 hundred you carried is 12 hundreds. If there are no more digits to add, just write 2 in the hundreds column and 1 in the thousands column to complete the answer.

	6	8	7
+	5	8	5
1	2	7	2
	1	1	

Now you try

1

	2	8	6
+	9	4	5
		3	1
		1	1

2

	4	6	5
+	1	8	5
		5	0
		1	1

3

	9	7	9
+	4	6	9
			8
		1	

4

	9	5	7
+	4	8	7
			4

5

	6	2	8
+	3	7	6

6

	8	8	9
+	9	7	4

More practice

Set out these questions yourself to answer them.

7 678 + 734 = ?

Th	H	T	U
+			

8 988 + 825 = ?

Th	H	T	U
+			

9 968 + 732 = ?

Th	H	T	U
+			

Problem solving

10 Work out the missing digit in this addition.

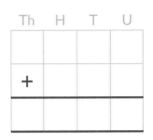

	4	◯	6
+	9	4	5
1	4	0	1

11 What is the sum of 865 and 567?

12 Kim has £479 in her bank account. She puts in £285 more. How much is in the account now?

13 A safari park had 356 visitors on Saturday and 476 on Sunday. How many visitors came in total that weekend?

How did I find Step 8? ☐ Easy ☐ OK ☐ Difficult

Step 9: Four-digit addition carrying once or twice

For the questions in this step, you will add four-digit numbers. Sometimes you will need to carry once and sometimes you will need to carry twice. In this example, both the units and hundreds digits have totals greater than 9.

Th	H	T	U
	6	7	4	4
+	1	5	3	9

What to do

6744 + 1539 = ?

1   Add the units digits. 4 + 9 = 13. Write the 3 in the units column and carry the ten units over to become 1 ten. Write 1 below the line, in the tens column.

Th	H	T	U
	6	7	4	4
+	1	5	3	9
				3

2   Then move left to add the tens digits and remember to add the 1 you carried. 4 tens + 3 tens plus the 1 ten carried is 8 tens.

Th	H	T	U
	6	7	4	4
+	1	5	3	9
			8	3

3   Now add the digits in the hundreds column. 7 hundreds + 5 hundreds is 12 hundreds. Write the 2 in the hundreds column and carry the 10 hundreds over to become 1 thousand. Write 1 below the line, in the thousands column.

Th	H	T	U
	6	7	4	4
+	1	5	3	9
		2	8	3

4   Now add the thousands and remember to add the 1 you carried. 6 thousands + 1 thousand plus the 1 thousand you carried is 8 thousands. Write 8 in the thousands column to complete the answer.

Th	H	T	U
	6	7	4	4
+	1	5	3	9
	8	2	8	3

Now you try

1

	4	6	2	9
+	1	2	8	3
			1	2

2

	3	8	2	7
+	1	6	1	4
				1

3

	6	2	7	5
+	1	3	6	8
				3

4

	4	8	5	3
+	1	7	6	2
				5

More practice

5
```
    5  2  9  4
 +  1  6  9  2
 _____
 _____
```

6
```
    4  5  8  3
 +  3  6  9  5
 _____
 _____
```

Set out these questions yourself to answer them.

7 2761 + 2263 = ?

Th	H	T	U
+			

8 3928 + 3567 = ?

Th	H	T	U
+			

Problem solving

9 Paul's income last year was £7378.
This year it has increased by £1535.
How much is it now?

_____

10 At a football match there were 2764
home fans and 1342 away fans.
How many fans were there altogether?

_____

11 Sales of the music track 'School's Out'
last week were 2815. This week sales
rose by 1475. How many were sold
this week?

_____

How did I find Step 9? ☐ Easy ☐ OK ☐ Difficult

Step 10: Three- and four-digit addition carrying once or twice, answers greater than 9999

These questions involve adding three- and four-digit numbers. Make sure you line up the digits in the correct columns. Sometimes the answers will be greater than 9999.

What to do

9634 + 871 = ?

1 Write the digits in the correct columns. Add the units digits.
4 + 1 = 5

TTh	Th	H	T	U
	9	6	3	4
+		8	7	1
				5

2 Then add the tens. 3 tens + 7 tens = 10 tens. Write 0 in the tens column and carry 10 tens over to become 1 hundred.

	9	6	3	4
+		8	7	1
			0	5

3 Now add the hundreds. 6 hundreds + 8 hundreds plus the 1 hundred carried is 15 hundreds. Write the 5 in the hundreds column and carry the 10 hundreds over to become 1 thousand.

	9	6	3	4
+		8	7	1
		5	0	5

4 Add the thousands to the 1 you carried. 9 thousands plus the 1 thousand carried is 10 thousands. Write 0 in the thousands column and 1 in the ten thousands column to complete the answer.

	9	6	3	4
+		8	7	1
1	0	5	0	5

Now you try

1

	9	7	8	4
+		7	4	5
			2	9

2

	4	8	2	6
+	6	8	7	1
				7

3

	9	5	3	4
+		7	2	8
				2

4

	7	9	6	7
+	7	4	7	1
				8

More practice

Set out these questions yourself to answer them.

5 9261 + 863 = ?

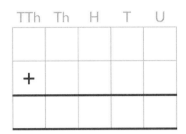

6 8925 + 3574 = ?

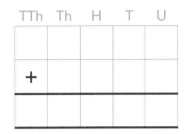

7 9346 + 2923 = ?

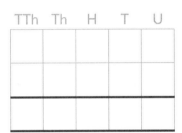

8 9823 + 757 = ?

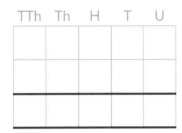

Problem solving

9 Phelim wants to buy a car and is looking at two of them. One costs £9574 and the other is £674 more. How much does the more expensive car cost?

10 8753 people visited the Multiplex cinema during one week in October. 2724 more than this visited in one week in November. How many visited in the November week?

How did I find Step 10? ☐ Easy ☐ OK ☐ Difficult

Step 11: Four-digit addition carrying three times

Now you're confident in carrying, you can do it several times. Here, these questions involve carrying three times. Some answers will also be over 9999.

What to do

$8634 + 4868 = ?$

1 Add the units digits and carry. $4 + 8 = 12$

TTh	Th	H	T	U
	8	6	3	4
+	4	8	6	8
				2

2 Then add the tens. 3 tens + 6 tens plus the 1 ten carried is 10 tens. Write 0 in the tens column and carry 10 tens over to become 1 hundred.

	8	6	3	4
+	4	8	6	8
			0	2

3 Now add the hundreds. 6 hundreds + 8 hundreds plus the 1 hundred carried is 15 hundreds. Write the 5 in the hundreds column and carry the 10 hundreds over to become 1 thousand.

	8	6	3	4
+	4	8	6	8
		5	0	2

4 Add the thousands. 8 thousands + 4 thousands plus the 1 thousand carried is 13 thousands. Write 3 in the thousands column and 1 in the ten thousands column to complete the answer.

	8	6	3	4
+	4	8	6	8
1	3	5	0	2

Now you try

1

	6	6	8	9
+	2	6	7	5
			6	4

2

	4	8	2	6
+	6	8	7	5
				1

3

	6	5	3	8
+	4	7	9	8
				6

4

	9	8	8	7
+	7	5	7	6

More practice

Set out these questions yourself to answer them.

5   9698 + 7863 = ?

TTh	Th	H	T	U

6   7975 + 3576 = ?

TTh	Th	H	T	U

Problem solving

7   A, B and C have been used to replace three digits in this addition. Can you work out the value of A, B and C?

	A	C	B	A
+	A	C	B	A
1	9	5	C	B

_____

8   A pilot flew 3752 miles in January and 4589 miles in February. How many miles did he fly altogether?

_____

9   What is the total of 5769 and 6856?

_____

10   Last year Sarah cycled 4337km. This year she cycled 1965km more than last year. How many kilometres did she cycle this year?

_____

How did I find Step 11?   ☐ Easy   ☐ OK   ☐ Difficult

Step 12: Addition of three numbers with three and four digits carrying up to three times

In this step, you'll add several numbers. Make sure you write the digits into the correct columns first. Remember to carry digits when necessary.

What to do

$8794 + 868 + 7642 = ?$

TTh	Th	H	T	U
	8	7	9	4
		8	6	8
+	7	6	4	2
				4
			1	

1   Add the units digits and carry. $4 + 8 + 2 = 14$

TTh	Th	H	T	U
	8	7	9	4
		8	6	8
+	7	6	4	2
			0	4
		2	1	

2   Then add the tens. 9 tens + 6 tens + 4 tens plus the 1 ten carried is 20 tens. Write 0 in the tens column and carry 20 tens over to become 2 hundreds.

TTh	Th	H	T	U
	8	7	9	4
		8	6	8
+	7	6	4	2
		3	0	4
	2	2	1	

3   Now add the hundreds. 7 hundreds + 8 hundreds + 6 hundreds plus the 2 hundreds carried is 23 hundreds. Write the 3 in the hundreds column and carry the 20 hundreds over to become 2 thousands.

TTh	Th	H	T	U
	8	7	9	4
		8	6	8
+	7	6	4	2
1	7	3	0	4
	2	2	1	

4   Add the thousands to the 2 thousands you carried. 8 thousands + 7 thousands plus the 2 thousands carried is 17 thousands. Write 7 in the thousands column and 1 in the ten thousands column to complete the answer.

Now you try

Set out these questions yourself to answer them.

1   $5886 + 697 + 975 = ?$

TTh	Th	H	T	U
	5	8	8	6
+				

2   $7864 + 2856 + 774 = ?$

TTh	Th	H	T	U
+				

More practice   Use the grid below for working.

3 2674 + 663 + 1845 = ?   _____

4 7841 + 4278 + 953 = ?   _____

5 7459 + 708 + 478 = ?   _____

6 9573 + 3867 + 858 = ?   _____

Problem solving

7 Choose a single digit greater than 3. Repeat it to make two four-digit numbers and a three-digit number. Then find the sum of the numbers, for example 4444 + 4444 + 444. Do this for 5, 6, 7, 8 and 9 too. What do you notice about the digits of the answers? Use spare paper for working.

_____

_____

How did I find Step 12?   ☐ Easy   ☐ OK   ☐ Difficult

Check-up test 2 Three- and four-digit addition, with up to three carries

Step 7

1 4855 + 1814 = ?

	4	8	5	5
+	1	8	1	4
				q

2 4335 + 2381 = ?

Step 8

3 627 + 377 = ?

	6	2	7
+	3	7	7

4 495 + 848 = ?

Step 9

5 5948 + 1731 = ?

	5	q	4	8
+	1	7	3	1

6 5761 + 2263 = ?

Steps 10 and 11

7 4439 + 497 = ?

	4	4	3	q
+		4	q	7

8 5452 + 2768 = ?

Step 12

Use the grid below for working.

9 2374 + 2265 + 845 = ? _____ ☐ 9

10 7664 + 725 + 1953 = ? _____ ☐ 10

Steps 7 to 12 mixed

Use the grid below for working.

11 What is the total of 5769 and 6856? _____ ☐ 11

12 The price of a TV that cost £757 was increased by £176. What is the new price? _____ ☐ 12

13 Add 668 to 1757. _____ ☐ 13

14 Which year was 945 years after the year 1066? _____ ☐ 14

Total test score

Score	1	2	3	4	5	6	7	8	9	10	11	12	13	14
%	7	14	21	29	36	43	50	57	64	71	79	86	93	100

☐ 14

Step 13: Five-digit addition carrying up to four times

What to do

1 Now that you're used to carrying, you can add larger and larger numbers. These questions involve adding five-digit numbers.

2 Just remember to work from right to left and carry digits when necessary.

HTh	TTh	Th	H	T	U
	5	9	6	3	4
+	6	7	8	7	1
1	2	7	5	0	5
		1	1	1	

Now you try

1

	3	7	6	3	4
+	6	7	2	4	9
					3
				1	

2

	4	5	7	3	8
+	7	3	5	7	3
					1
				1	

3

	6	6	3	8	4
+	3	5	8	7	2
					6

4

	5	9	6	3	6
+	4	5	4	7	4

5

	9	9	2	2	7
+	7	3	6	8	4

6

	8	5	4	9	9
+	8	7	4	2	0

More practice

7
```
    8 4 5 0 6
 +  1 4 8 9 6
 _____
```

8
```
    7 7 7 7 7
 +  7 7 7 7 7
 _____
```

Set out these questions yourself to answer them.

9 79 837 + 57 842 = ?

HTh	TTh	Th	H	T	U
+					

10 59 094 + 71 887 = ?

HTh	TTh	Th	H	T	U
+					

Problem solving

11 Palindromic numbers are those that are the same when the digits are written in reverse order, like 15551 or 23532. Use two digits to make two palindromic numbers, for example 37773 and 73337. Add them to find the total. Is the answer palindromic? Try other digits in the same way. Can you find any palindromic answers? Use spare paper for working.

_____

_____

12 25 753 fans were at a football stadium to see a match and 94 545 fans watched it on TV. How many saw the match in total?

_____

How did I find Step 13?   ☐ Easy   ☐ OK   ☐ Difficult

Step 14: Addition of a list of numbers

It is important to be able to add a long list of numbers. Make sure when you set out the addition that you write the digits into the correct columns first.

What to do

Find the sum of 47353, 573, 6856, 252 and 12453.

HTh	TTh	Th	H	T	U
	4	7	3	5	3
			5	7	3
		6	8	5	6
			2	5	2
+	1	2	4	5	3
	6	7	4	8	7
	1	2	2	1	

1 Line up the digits correctly.

2 Then work from right to left, adding the digits in each column and carrying if necessary. Look for pairs or sets of numbers that total 10 to help you add them.

3 Remember to add the carried digit when adding the digits in the next column.

Now you try   Set out these questions yourself to answer them.

1 Find the total of 54845, 8346, 9487, 171 and 14653.

HTh	TTh	Th	H	T	U
	5	4	8	4	5
+					

2 Find the sum of 8243, 25573, 1256, 609 and 81253.

HTh	TTh	Th	H	T	U
+					

More practice   Use the grid below for working.

3   21 574 + 663 + 1845 + 53 524 + 3442 = ?   _____

4   5459 + 17 308 + 478 + 6846 + 88 445 = ?   _____

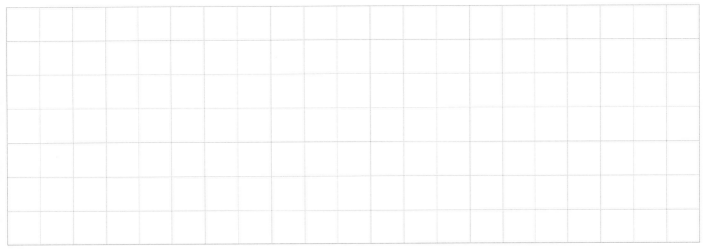

Problem solving

5   Use spare paper to find the sum of 11 111, 22 222, 33 333, 44 444 and 55 555.
Write the answer in digits and in words.

_____

_____

6   This table shows the number of copies
of a newspaper that was sold each day.
Find the total number sold in the week.

Mon	Tues	Wed	Thurs	Fri	Sat	Sun
6846	4675	8465	4662	5102	18352	25432

_____

How did I find Step 14?   ☐ Easy   ☐ OK   ☐ Difficult

Step 15: Large number addition

What to do

1 You've learnt how to do written addition for numbers with up to five digits. Adding even larger numbers is just as easy!

2 Remember to work from right to left and carry digits when necessary.

	HTh	TTh	Th	H	T	U
	5	0	6	6	4	1
+	2	4	8	2	7	3
	7	5	4	9	1	4
				1		1

Now you try

1 Seven hundred and nine thousand, three hundred and seventeen plus thirty-one thousand, four hundred and forty-six.

	HTh	TTh	Th	H	T	U
	7	0	9	3	1	7
+		3	1	4	4	6

2 Nine hundred and twenty thousand, three hundred and fifty add six hundred and eighty-two thousand and eighteen.

	M	HTh	TTh	Th	H	T	U
		9	2	0	3	5	0
+	6	8	2	0	1	8

3 Eight hundred thousand, five hundred and twelve plus two hundred and sixty thousand, two hundred and nineteen.

	M	HTh	TTh	Th	H	T	U
		8	0	0	5	1	2
+	2	6	0	2	1	9

4 Two hundred and sixty-one thousand, nine hundred and three add ninety-four thousand, six hundred and seven.

	HTh	TTh	Th	H	T	U
	2	6	1	9	0	3
+		9	4	6	0	7

More practice

Set out these questions yourself to answer them.

5 Six hundred and ninety thousand and thirty-nine plus seventy-eight thousand, two hundred and forty-one.

	HTh	TTh	Th	H	T	U
+						

6 Five hundred and twelve thousand and forty-six add six hundred and nine thousand and sixty-five.

	M	HTh	TTh	Th	H	T	U
+							

Problem solving

7 Can you work out which digit the letter A stands for in this addition?

_____

	9	A	8	A	7	5
+	6	8	2	8	A	6
1	6	3	1	3	2	1

8 Two large schools raised money for a children's charity. One school raised £385 057 and the other raised £184 488. How much did they give to the charity altogether?

9 Over a season, 573 684 adults and 375 427 children went to watch the matches of a football team. What was the total attendance?

How did I find Step 15?   ☐ Easy   ☐ OK   ☐ Difficult

Check-up test 3 Addition of large numbers

Step 13

1   44 638 + 74 677 = ?

	4	4	6	3	8
+	7	4	6	7	7

2   69 094 + 71 887 = ?

□ 1
□ 2

Step 14

3   Find the sum of 67 354, 573, 6856, 252 and 12 453.

	6	7	3	5	4
			5	7	3
		6	8	5	6
			2	5	2
+	1	2	4	5	3

4   Find the sum of 9354, 25 473, 1256, 509 and 81 253.

□ 3
□ 4

Step 15

5   Nine hundred and twenty-seven thousand, three hundred and fifty plus six hundred and eighty-two thousand, eight hundred and eighteen.

	9	2	7	3	5	0
+	6	8	2	8	1	8

6   Five hundred and twelve thousand and thirty-nine plus seven hundred and nine thousand and sixty-five.

+						

□ 5
□ 6

Steps 13 to 15 mixed

Use the grid below for working.

7 54 753 fans were at a football stadium to see a match and 58 545 fans watched it on TV. How many saw the match in total? _____ ☐ 7

8 Over a season 439 684 adults and 327 427 children went to watch the matches of a hockey team. What was the total attendance? _____ ☐ 8

9 This table shows the number of children attending a school each day. Find the total attendance for the week. _____ ☐ 9

Mon	2342
Tues	2355
Wed	2314
Thurs	2347
Fri	2338

Total test score

Score	1	2	3	4	5	6	7	8	9
%	11	22	33	44	56	67	78	89	100

☐ 9

Step 16: Decimal addition one decimal place

Now that you can add whole numbers, adding decimals is almost as easy! All you need to do is to set out the digits in the correct columns and add in the same way!

Th	H	T	U	.	t
	3	4	4	.	5
+		1	8	.	4

$344.5 + 18.4 = ?$

What to do

1 Start with the right-hand column, the tenths.
5 tenths + 4 tenths = 9 tenths

Th	H	T	U	.	t
	3	4	4	.	5
+		1	8	.	4
				.	9

2 Then move to the units. 4 + 8 = 12. Write 2 and carry the 10.

Th	H	T	U	.	t
	3	4	4	.	5
+		1	8	.	4
			2	.	9

3 Continue working left to complete the addition. Remember to put the decimal point in your answer, in line with the decimal points above.

Th	H	T	U	.	t
	3	4	4	.	5
+		1	8	.	4
	3	6	2	.	9

Now you try

1 $5197.4 + 432.7 = ?$

	5	1	9	7	.	4
+		4	3	2	.	7
					.	1

2 $455.9 + 78.4 = ?$

	4	5	5	.	9
+		7	8	.	4
					3

3 $3527.4 + 1278.3 = ?$

	3	5	2	7	.	4
+	1	2	7	8	.	3

4 $704.3 + 437.9 = ?$

	7	0	4	.	3
+	4	3	7	.	9

More practice

Set out these questions yourself to answer them.

5 8526.4 + 495.8 = ?

	Th	H	T	U	.	t
+						

6 8763.1 + 532.7 = ?

	Th	H	T	U	.	t
+						

Problem solving

7 Melina runs 67.6km in January and 7.7km further than this in February. How far does she run in February?

8 In an 800m athletics race, the time of the fastest runner was 156.6 seconds. The slowest runner took 18.9 seconds longer. How long did the slowest runner take?

9 After going on a diet, Sam weighed 78.8kg. Before the diet his weight had been 13.5kg more than this. How much did he weigh before the diet?

How did I find Step 16? ☐ Easy ☐ OK ☐ Difficult

Step 17: Decimal addition two decimal places

Here you will add numbers with two decimal places.
Remember to set out the digits in the correct columns.

	H	T	U	.	t	h
		1	6	2 .	3	8
+			1	8 .	6	7

What to do

$162.38 + 18.67 = ?$

1   Start with the right-hand column. 8 hundredths
+ 7 hundredths is 15 hundredths. Write the
5 hundredths and carry the 10 hundredths as 1 tenth.

	H	T	U	.	t	h
		1	6	2 .	3	8
+			1	8 .	6	7
						5
						1

2   3 tenths + 6 tenths plus the 1 tenth carried is 10 tenths.
Write the 0. Carry the 10 tenths as 1 unit.

		1	6	2 .	3	8
+			1	8 .	6	7
					0	5
				1	1	

3   Then move to the units. 2 + 8 plus the 1 carried is 11.
Write 1 and carry the ten.

		1	6	2 .	3	8
+			1	8 .	6	7
			1	0	5	
		1	1	1		

4   Continue working left to complete the addition.
Remember to put the decimal point in your answer,
in line with the decimal points above.

		1	6	2 .	3	8
+			1	8 .	6	7
1	8	1 .	0	5		
	1	1	1			

Now you try

1 $513.64 + 131.77 = ?$

	5	1	3 .	6	4
+	1	3	1 .	7	7
					1
			1		

2 $235.94 + 67.84 = ?$

	2	3	5 .	9	4
+		6	7 .	8	4
					8

More practice

3

```
    7  4  5 . 6  4
+   1  2  8 . 6  5
_____
```

4

```
    8  8  8 . 8  8
+         2  3 . 4  3
_____
```

Set out these questions yourself to answer them.

5 652.74 + 195.84 = ?

H	T	U .	t	h
+				

6 832.19 + 53.87 = ?

H	T	U .	t	h
+				

Problem solving

7 Jack has £546.45 in his bank account. His wages of £375.33 are also paid into this account. How much money does he have now?

_____

8 What is 37.68ml more than 125.55ml?

_____

9 A baby weighed 3.46kg at birth. At six months old he had gained 4.88kg. How much did he weigh when he was six months old?

_____

| **How did I find Step 17?** | ☐ Easy | ☐ OK | ☐ Difficult |

Step 18: Decimal addition different numbers of decimal places

What to do

In this last step, the questions have different numbers of decimal places so you must be careful to write the digits in the correct columns. Sometimes it can help to write zeros in the empty spaces. Don't forget to put the decimal point in your answer each time!

Now you try   Set out these questions yourself to answer them.

1 492.76 + 16.825 = ?

H	T	U .	t	h	th
	4	9	2 . 7	6	0
+		1	6 . 8	2	5
					5

2 205.7 + 52.139 = ?

H	T	U .	t	h	th
	2	0	5 . 7	0	0
+					

3 842.9 + 9.82 = ?

4 78.135 + 38.66 = ?

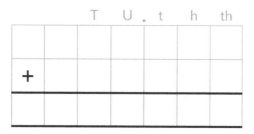

5 908.8 + 174.631 = ?

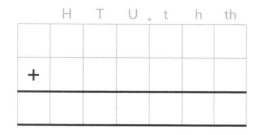

6 809.3 + 562.89 = ?

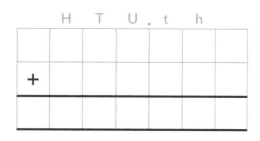

More practice

Set out these questions yourself to answer them. Check your answers by subtracting.

7 4653.75 + 2854.56 = ?

8 406.90 + 384.73 = ?

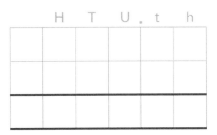

Problem solving

9 Kay went on holiday. During the first week she spent £183.87 and in the second week she spent £275.90. How much more than £450 did she spend in total?

_____

10 Usain Bolt ran 100m in 9.572 seconds. This was 1.228 seconds faster than the world record holder in 1891. How many seconds did the world record holder in 1891 take?

_____

11 What is special about the sum of 304.28 litres and 251.275 litres?

_____

_____

How did I find Step 18? Easy OK ☐ Difficult

Final test Addition of whole numbers and decimals

Steps 16 to 18

1 7526.5 + 495.7 = ?

+
_____

2 3727.4 + 1278.9 = ?

+
_____

3 567.27 + 164.58 = ?

+
_____

4 828.36 + 55.29 = ?

+
_____

5 742.9 + 16.826 = ?

+
_____

6 55.134 + 28.77 = ?

+
_____

Use the grid below for working.

7 A parcel weighs 2.78kg. Another parcel weighs
1.34kg more. How much does it weigh?   _____

8 Add 90.92 to 902.9.   _____